SRA Open Court Reading

Stick to It

A Division of The McGraw·Hill Companies

Columbus, Ohio

Program Authors

Marilyn Jager Adams

Carl Bereiter

Anne McKeough

Robbie Case

Marsha Roit

Jan Hirshberg

Iva Carruthers

Gerald H. Treadway, Jr.

Acknowledgements

Egmont Children's Books: THE GREAT BIG ENORMOUS TURNIP by Alexei Tolstoy, illustrations by Helen Oxenbury. Illustrations copyright © 1968 by Helen Oxenbury. Reproduced by kind permission of Egmont Children's Books. HarperCollins Publishers: "TO CATCH A FISH" from UNDER THE SUNDAY TREE by ELOISE GREENFIELD, illustrations by MR. AMOS FERGUSON. TEXT COPYRIGHT © 1988 BY ELOISE GREENFIELD. ILLUSTRATIONS COPYRIGHT © 1988 BY AMOS FERGUSON. Used by permission of HarperCollins Publishers. Alfred A. Knopf, Inc.: **TILLIE AND THE WALL by Leo Lionni. Copyright © 1989 by Leo Lionni.** Reprinted by arrangement with Alfred A. Knopf, Inc.

SRA/McGraw-Hill

A Division of The **McGraw·Hill** *Companies*

Send all inquiries to:
SRA/McGraw-Hill
8787 Orion Place
Columbus, OH 43240-4027

Printed in the United States of America.

ISBN 0-02-830933-2

3 4 5 6 7 8 9 SCG 04 03 02 01 00

Table *of* Contents

Stick to It

The Great Big Enormous
Turnip

Alexei Tolstoy

illustrated by Helen Oxenbury

O nce upon a time an old man
planted a little turnip and said, "Grow,
grow, little turnip, grow sweet. Grow,
grow, little turnip, grow strong."

And the turnip grew up sweet and strong, and big and enormous. Then, one day, the old man went to pull it up. He pulled and pulled again, but he could not pull it up.

He called the old woman.

The old woman pulled the old man.
The old man pulled the turnip. And they
pulled and pulled again, but they could
not pull it up.

So the old woman called her
granddaughter.

The granddaughter pulled the old woman, the old woman pulled the old man, the old man pulled the turnip. And they pulled and pulled again, but they could not pull it up.

The granddaughter called the black dog.

The black dog pulled the granddaughter, the granddaughter pulled the old woman, the old woman pulled the old man, the old man pulled the turnip. And they pulled and pulled again, but they could not pull it up.

The black dog called the cat.

The cat pulled the dog. The dog pulled the granddaughter, the granddaughter pulled the old woman, the old woman pulled the old man, the old man pulled the turnip. And they pulled and pulled again, but still they could not pull it up.

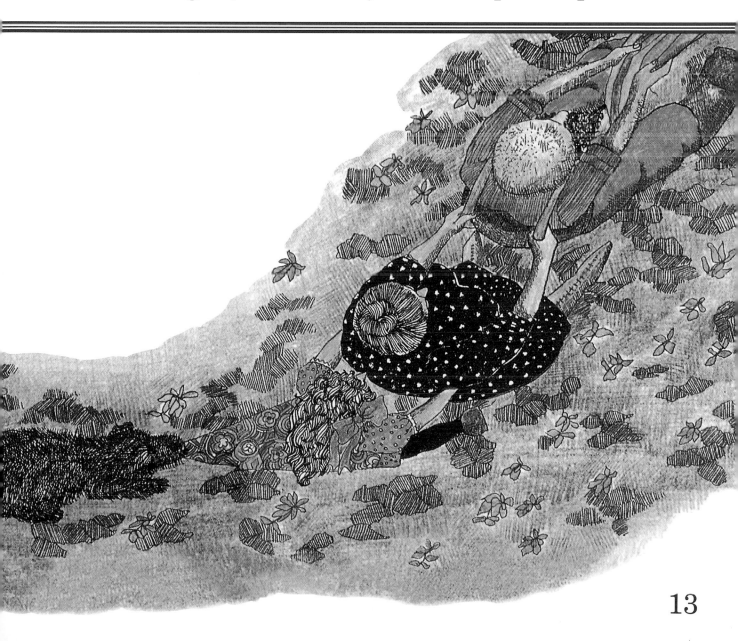

The cat called the mouse.

The mouse pulled the cat, the cat pulled the dog, the dog pulled the granddaughter, the granddaughter pulled the old woman, the old woman pulled the old man, the old man pulled the turnip.

They pulled and pulled again, and up came the turnip at last.

To Catch a Fish

from UNDER THE SUNDAY TREE
Eloise Greenfield
illustrated by Mr. Amos Ferguson

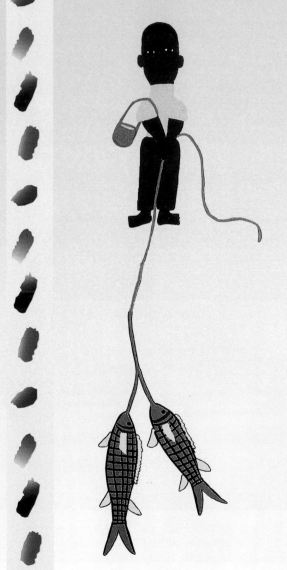

It takes more than a wish
to catch a fish
you take the hook
you add the bait
you concentrate
and then you wait
you wait you wait
but not a bite
the fish don't have
an appetite

so tell them what
good bait you've got
and how your bait
can hit the spot
this works a whole
lot better than
a wish
if you really
want to catch
a fish

Tillie and the Wall

by Leo Lionni

The wall had been there ever since the mice could remember. They never paid attention to it.

They never asked themselves what was on the other side, nor, for that matter, if there were another side at all.

They went about their business as if
the wall didn't exist.

The mice loved to talk. They chatted endlessly about this and that, but no one ever mentioned the wall.

Only Tillie, the youngest, would stare at it,
wondering about the other side.

At night, while the others were asleep, she would lie in her bed of straw, wide awake, imagining beyond the wall a beautiful, fantastic world inhabited by strange animals and plants.

"We *must* see the other side," she told her friends. "Let us try to climb." They tried, but as they climbed, the wall seemed higher and higher.

With a long, rusty nail they tried to
make a hole to peep through. "It is only
a question of patience!" said Tillie.

But after working an entire
morning they gave up, exhausted,
without having made even a dent
in the hard stone.

28

"The wall must end *somewhere*,"
Tillie said. They walked and walked
for many hours. The wall apparently
had no end.

But one day, not far from the wall, Tillie saw a worm digging itself into the black earth. How could she not have thought of that before? Why hadn't anyone thought of that before?

Full of excitement, Tillie began to dig.
She dug and she dug . . .

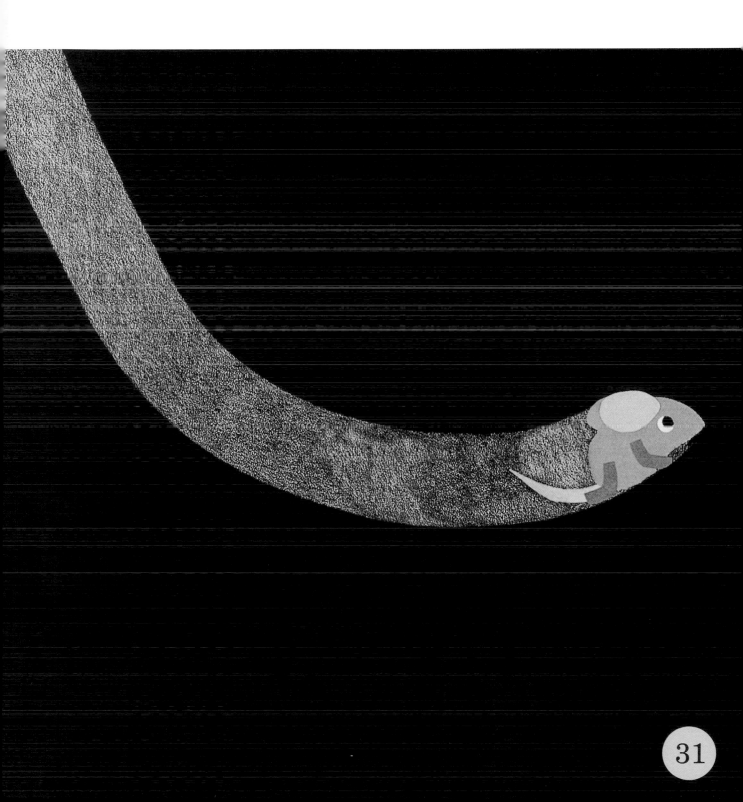

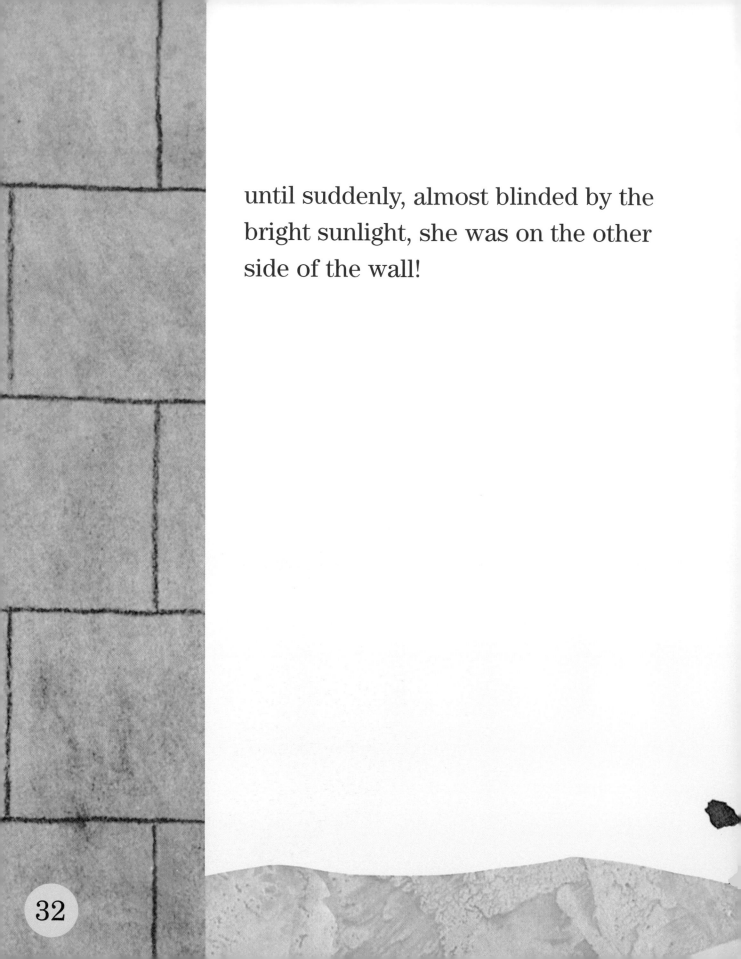

until suddenly, almost blinded by the bright sunlight, she was on the other side of the wall!

She couldn't believe her eyes: before her were mice, regular mice.

The mice gave Tillie a great welcome party. They took her to their celebration pebble (had she seen that before somewhere?).

They made speeches
in her honor and waved
flags.

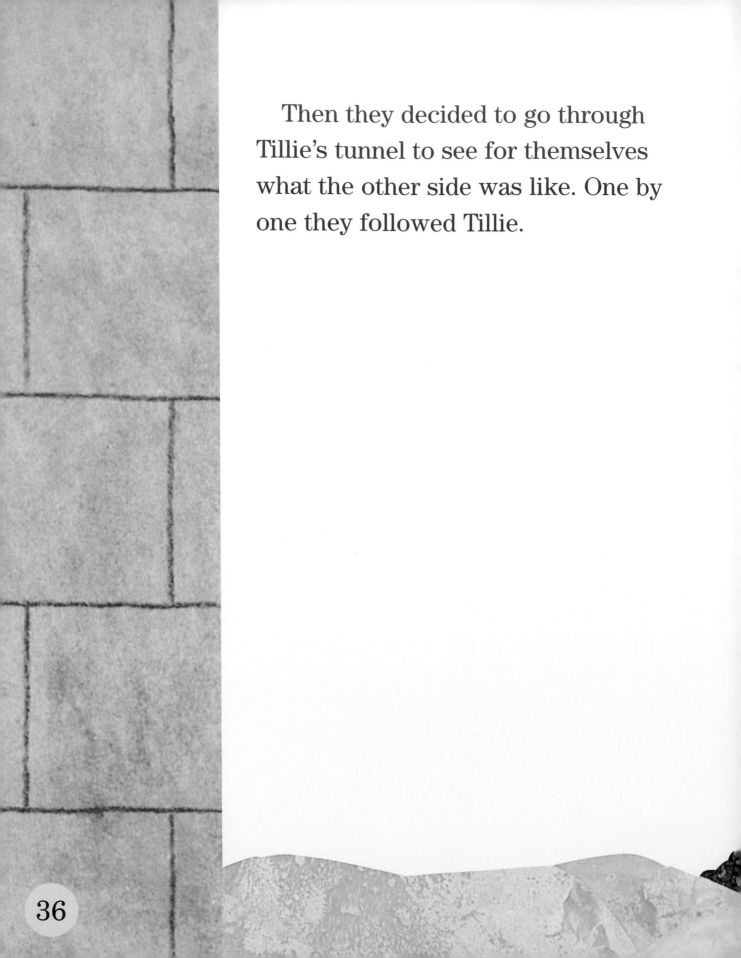

Then they decided to go through Tillie's tunnel to see for themselves what the other side was like. One by one they followed Tillie.

And when the mice on Tillie's side of the wall saw what Tillie had discovered, there was another party.

The mice threw confetti. Everyone
shouted "TIL-LIE, TIL-LIE, TIL-LIE!"
and they carried Tillie high in the air in
triumph.

Since that day the mice go freely
from one side of the wall to the other,
and they always remember that it was
Tillie who first showed them the way.

FINE Art

***The House of Cards.* Zinaida Serebriakova.**
Russian State Museum, St. Petersburg, Russia.
Photo: Scala/Art Resource, NY.

***Bicycle Race.* Arthur Sollberger.** Private
Collection. Photo: Bridgeman Art Library.

***Boy Juggling Shells.* Edo period.
Katsushika Hokusai.** Album leaf,
ink and color on paper. $13 \frac{15}{16} \times 9 \frac{1}{2}$ in.
The Metropolitan Museum of Art,
Charles Stewart Smith Collection, Gift
of Mrs. Charles Stewart Smith,
Charles Stewart Smith, Jr. and
Howard Caswell Smith, in memory
of Charles Stewart Smith, 1914
(14.76.59). Photograph ©1996 The
Metropolitan Museum of Art.

40